HOUGHTON MIFFLIN

Reading
A Legacy of Literacy

Wheels Go Around

HOUGHTON MIFFLIN   BOSTON • MORRIS PLAINS, NJ

California • Colorado • Georgia • Illinois • New Jersey • Texas

Printed in the U.S.A.

ISBN: 0-618-16193-7

3456789-BS-06 05 04 03 02

Design, Art Management, and Page Production: Studio Goodwin Sturges

Contents

Big Rig

by Amy Griffin
illustrated by Bob Kolar

Big Rig can dig.

Dig, dig, dig.

Big Rig can dig a pit.

Big Rig can dig a pit
for Dan.

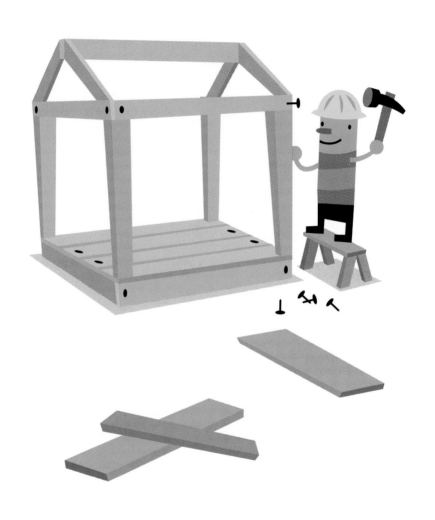

Dan can .

Dan can  .
Big Rig can dig.

Tan Van

by Amy Griffin

illustrated by Amiko Hirao

It is a tan van!

Zig Pig ran.
Can I have it?

Dan Cat ran.
Can I have it?

Zig Pig sat.
Dan Cat sat.

Zig Pig and Dan Cat

by Amy Griffin
illustrated by Amiko Hirao

Zig Pig and Dan Cat
dig for 🐚 .

Zig Pig can dig.
I have it!

Dan Cat can dig.
Here it is!

Zig Pig sat.
Dan Cat sat.

Word List

Theme 7, Week 1
Big Rig

DECODABLE WORDS

Target Skill
Consonant *d:*
Dan, dig

Words Using Previously Taught Skills
Big, can, Dan, dig, Rig, pit

HIGH-FREQUENCY WORDS

New
for

Previously Taught
a

Theme 7, Week 2
Tan Van

DECODABLE WORDS

Target Skill
Consonant *z:*
Zig

Words Using Previously Taught Skills
can, Cat, Dan, it, ran, Pig, sat, tan, van, Zig

HIGH-FREQUENCY WORDS

New
have

Previously Taught
a, I, is

Theme 7, Week 3
Zig Pig and Dan Cat

DECODABLE WORDS

Words Using Previously Taught Skills
can, Cat, Dan, dig, it, Pig, sat, Zig

HIGH-FREQUENCY WORDS

Previously Taught
and, for, have, here, I, is

HIGH-FREQUENCY WORDS TAUGHT TO DATE

a	here	see
and	I	to
for	is	
go	like	
have	my	

Decoding Skills Taught to Date Consonant *b*, consonant *c*, consonant *d*, consonant *f*, consonant *g*, consonant *h*, consonant *k*, consonant *l*, consonant *m*, consonant *n*, consonant *q*, consonant *r*, consonant *s*, consonant *t*, consonant *v*, consonant *z*, short *a*, short *i*